California State Capitol

Time Machine

Coloring Book

Illustrations by William G. Wolf
Designed and Written by Loraine B. Donnelly

California Capital Enterprises

State Capitol Construction
1860 – 1874

The Time Machine whirls us back to the years 1860 – 1874.

Work on the Capitol's foundation cannot begin until the ground level is raised 13 feet above the street as protection against flooding (a common occurrence in downtown Sacramento during this period). In May, 1861, the cornerstone is laid and construction begins.

The exterior walls of the first story are built of light and dark granite hauled in railroad cars from nearby Rocklin and Folsom. The second and third stories, 30″ thick, are made of brick set in mortar (a mixture of lime with sand and water) and covered with white plaster.

For 14 years construction continues, as work stops each winter due to rain. Finally, with completion of the roof in 1869, 40 Senators and 80 Assemblymen occupy the Capitol for the first time. A Grand Ball is held that year in both the Assembly and Senate chambers, but construction continues.

The Capitol is finally completed in 1874, at a cost of $2,500,000. Special taxes are levied to cover the cost, which is more than the initial estimate.

State Capitol Circa (about) 1885

The Capitol building towers over the city of Sacramento.

Senate Chambers

In 1869 a Grand Ball is held in the chambers of the two houses of the Legislature, to celebrate completion of the Capitol. Attending are the Senators, the Assemblymen, their ladies and guests, who enjoy the dancing and refreshments.

The Ornamental Stairs

After the Grand Ball, a Senator and his lady descend the stairs, with gas-powered lights showing the way.
The stairs themselves and each of the posts with carved bear heads were finished just before the Capitol opened.

Assembly Chambers

In December, 1869, 80 Assemblymen (and 40 Senators in the Senate chambers), sitting at hand-carved desks beneath gas-lit chandeliers, open the first legislative session in the new building.

The Eureka Tiles

In 1869 each Eureka emblem of 320 tiles is installed at 4 locations on the first floor of the Capitol. These emblems contain some of the symbols included in the Great Seal (see Great Seal page).

The Rotunda

On the black and white marble tile floor is a statue presented to the state in 1883 by a Sacramento banker, Mr. D.O. Mills. Carved in marble by a famous American sculptor, Larkin G. Mead, it depicts Columbus, on bended knee, asking the Queen of Spain to finance his voyage to the New World.

Governor George C. Pardee's Administration
January 7, 1903 – January 8, 1907

The Time Machine advances to the years 1903 – 1907.

Elected as the 21st Governor of the State of California in November of 1902, George C. Pardee, native-born and former mayor of the City of Oakland, is also a physician.

Though the Southern Pacific Railroad supported his nomination for Governor, Pardee now tends to oppose the corporations that have dominated state politics. He presses for reforms in state finance, conservation and education.

He succeeds in levying new taxes on corporations and a direct inheritance tax. He favors a constitutional amendment to permit the State Treasurer to deposit state funds in bank accounts to earn interest (implemented in 1907).

In his medical student days in Germany, he was impressed by that country's forest management. Now, as Governor, he succeeds in having the legislature establish the state's first Forestry Program (1905).

Education is a prime concern. The Governor has just finished writing a chapter on vaccinations for a state textbook on hygiene. His long interest in higher education is apparent — he received both a Bachelor's and Master's degree from the University of California at Berkeley. As Governor he is personally involved in selecting the small town of Davis as the site of an agricultural college and university (1906).

Governor Pardee showed his concern for the prisoners and mental patients in state institutions by sometimes personally responding to their letters.

He is widely known for his "open door policy," and is always willing to meet and talk with visitors, regardless of their political party.

Governor Pardee's Reception Room of 1906

Cords hanging from the "gasolier" bring power to the desk lamp and the telephone. (Electric-powered tulip globes were added to the gasoliers in 1892.) In front of the marble fireplace, a coal-burning stove provides the heat for this 20′ high room.

Governor's Main Office of 1906

Governor Pardee greets visitors to his office. Californians are able to meet and discuss their concerns directly with the Governor. When a great disaster strikes San Francisco, Governor Pardee leaves this office to establish a temporary one in Oakland.

Earthquake in San Francisco

April 18, 1906 — Earthquake strikes; San Francisco in flames! The city burns for 4 days. Smoke pours from the wooden homes and buildings. Gas and water lines are broken. People are ordered to cook in the streets, while smoke from the fires darkens the sky. More than 3,000 are dead and 250,000 homeless. San Francisco is in ruins.

Governor's Private Office of 1906

Governor Pardee is back in the Capitol for a special session of the Legislature, dealing with problems of the San Francisco earthquake.

Secretary of State's Office, 1902

Charles Curry, Secretary of State, sits at his desk (left) reading election returns. Posters on the wall show the successful Republican candidates in the 1902 election, including Governor Pardee and Secretary Curry. The only woman in this office — Minerva, Secretary Curry's sister — mails out driver's license badges: fee — $2.

Treasurer's Office of 1906

Each day a Wells Fargo man hauls into this office bags of gold to be deposited in the state's vault (next to the safe). Each bag holds 1,000 twenty dollar gold pieces, or $20,000. Nearly $7,000,000 in gold and silver is in the vault (the state does not accept paper money).

Attorney General's Office of 1906

Law clerks are studying insurance laws. Governor Pardee has asked this office to investigate the insurance situation relative to the earthquake. With the Attorney General's San Francisco Office destroyed, all investigations and prosecutions are conducted from this office.

The Great Seal of California

On the second floor of the Capitol, a stained glass depiction of the Great Seal of California is set into the ceiling above the entrance doors to both the Senate and the Assembly chambers.

Across the blue sky at the top of the Seal are 31 stars, one for each state in the Union after California — the 31st state — was admitted.

Below the stars the Greek word "Eureka," meaning "I have found it," recalls the discovery of gold in California in 1848.

The Sierra Nevada mountains — snow-capped in some versions of the Seal — are a symbol of California's grandeur.

The sailing ships in San Francisco Bay stand for commerce and trade.

The helmeted Roman Goddess of Wisdom, Minerva (whose Greek counterpart, Athena, was said to have sprung full-grown from the brow of Zeus), represents California's direct admission to statehood, without having served the customary period as a "territory."

The Grizzly Bear represents our animal wildlife, and some versions of the Seal also include a grapevine, standing for agriculture.

The design of the Great Seal was approved at the State Constitutional Convention in 1849, but we do not know the year in which the stained glass seals were first installed in the Capitol. We do know, however, that both seals were made by a San Francisco glass factory between 1907 and 1908.

THE GREAT SEAL OF THE STATE OF CALIFORNIA

EUREKA

The State Capitol Restored

1975 – 1982

The Time Machine stops at January, 1982. During a week-long celebration complete with fireworks and kleig lights, Californians pay homage to their new star attraction — the restored State Capitol.

In 1975, the Capitol had been declared unsafe for occupancy, due to fears that it might collapse in case of an earthquake. Proposals were made to construct a modern Capitol, but the legislature wisely recognized the importance of preserving this part of California's heritage.

The work began in 1975 with the systematic removal of everything within, until only the original brick walls remained. Those walls were reinforced with steel anchors and a 36″ thick floor was laid over the original foundation. Artisans using parts of the original Capitol and historic photographs created once again the interior as it was known to its earlier occupants.

After six years and a cost of $67.5 million (about $2 for each Californian), the work was finished and the beauty of the 1900 – 1910 period restored.

California's Capitol building may be unique among state capitols. Not only do Senators and Assemblymen meet here to enact legislation, but with the restoration completed, the Capitol also became a museum. The refurbished offices of Governor George C. Pardee's administration, facing the hallways of the west wing, comprise the State Capitol Museum.

Today, the Capitol proudly welcomes millions of visitors annually from every state in the Union, as well as from many foreign lands.

Gala Celebration – January 1982

Fireworks illuminate the Capitol's dome during the Gala Celebration for the restored Capitol.

Official Emblems of California

Reptile — **Desert Tortoise.** A long-lived vegetarian, it digs a deep burrow which it shares with rattlesnakes.

Fish — **Golden Trout.** Found only in the icy streams of the Sierra Nevada. It has yellowish underparts, reddish fins and a reddish stripe on its sides.

Insect — **Dog-face Butterfly.** Found only in California, its upper wings are black with dark orange trim and its lower wings are bright yellow with light orange trim.

Tree — **Redwood, both Coastal and Sierra.** They are ancient giant trees found only in California and Oregon.

Flower — **Golden Poppy.** Their yellow and orange blooms flower somewhere in California throughout the year. April 6 is California Poppy Day.

Bird — **Valley Quail,** which is found throughout the state. It has a brown back and a light blue breast, speckled with brown and tan.

Flag — **Bear Flag,** which was first raised in 1846 by American settlers in revolt against Mexico (to which California then belonged).

Fossil — **Saber-tooth Cat.** Common in California 40 million years ago, it was a tiger-sized animal with 8″ fangs.

Marine Mammal — **Gray Whale.** Thirty to fifty feet long, it is often seen along the coast during its 14,000 mile migration to and from Baja, California and the Arctic.

Gemstone — **Benitoite Sapphire.** A blue stone, found in San Benito County.

Dance — **West Coast Swing Dance.** Also known as the Swing, Whip or Jitterbug, it is danced to American music and originated in the 1930s in California. Officially designated in 1988.

Folk Dance — **Square Dance.** The familiar American folk dance, common in California since the Gold Rush. Officially designated in 1988.

Official Emblems of California

REPTILE

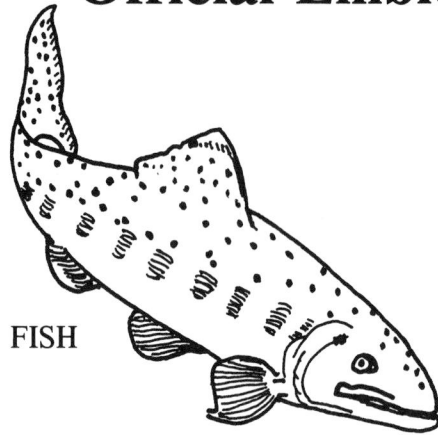

FISH

INSECT

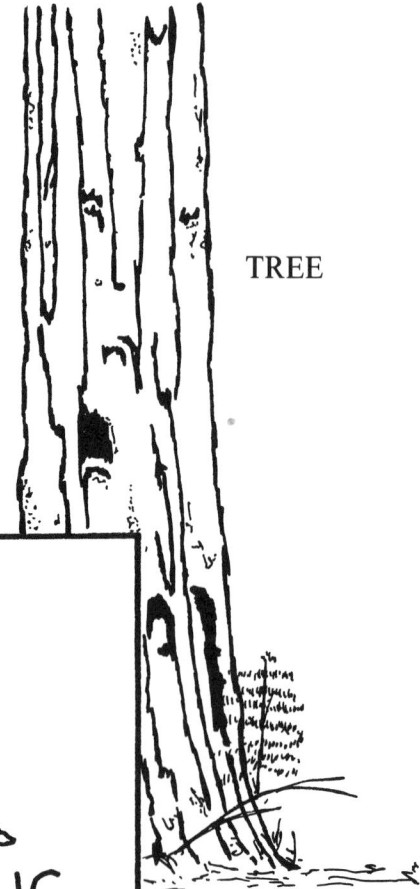

TREE

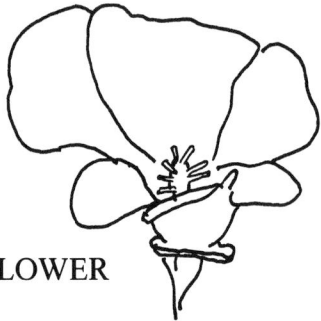

FLOWER

BIRD

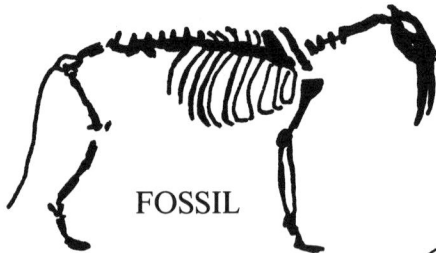

FOSSIL

FLAG

CALIFORNIA REPUBLIC

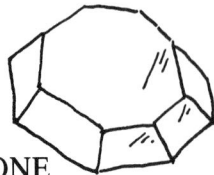

GEMSTONE

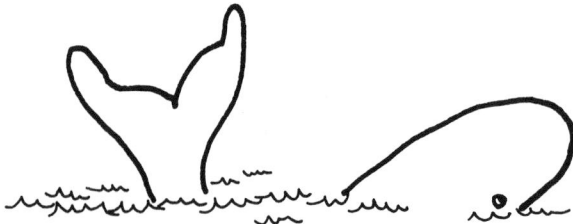

MARINE MAMMAL

DANCE

FOLK DANCE

Official Emblems of California

Motto — **"Eureka,"** a Greek word meaning "I have found it," referring to the discovery of gold.

Nickname— **The Golden State.** California's prosperity began with the gold rush.

Colors — **Blue and gold ribbons,** used with the Great Seal. These are also the colors of the University of California.

Song — **"I love you, California"** was declared the official state song in 1988.

Mineral — **Gold.** More gold has been found here than in any other state.

Rock — **Serpentine.** Found throughout California. Usually dull green with red and brown blotches due to its iron content.

Animal — **Grizzly Bear,** which appears on the State Flag and in the Great Seal. Though once widespread, they are no longer found in California.

MOTTO

NICKNAME

COLORS

SONG

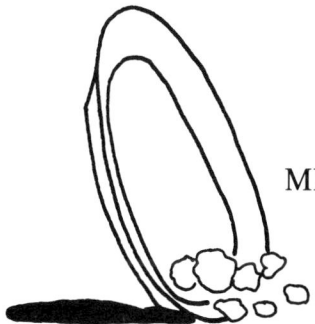

MINERAL

ROCK

ANIMAL

Newest Official Emblem — Prehistoric Artifact

The
Chipped Stone Bear
was designated
California's Official Prehistoric Artifact in 1991.

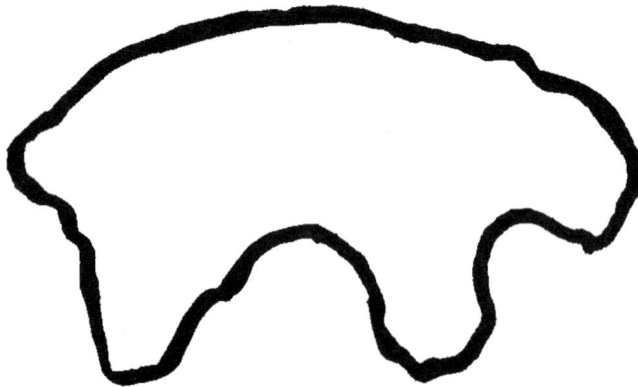

Measuring 2 -1/2", it was found by archeology students during a scientific dig in San Diego County. The specimen was fashioned by Native Americans nearly 8,000 years ago, making it one of the earliest examples of representational art discovered in California.